ABOUT THE COVER: *The colorful harlequin beetle of tropical South America has a body about 2½ inches long, while its front legs and antennae are about 3 inches long. The tiny scorpions on the beetle's abdomen eat the mites which infest the beetle's body—an example of the mutually beneficial relationship known as symbiosis.*

FRONT ENDSHEETS: *Insect life on a California dune. From left to right: two oil beetles; a digger wasp catching a syrphus fly to feed its young; a wool bee's nest lined with little pebbles; a red click beetle; a wingless leafhopper.*

THE INSECT WORLD

WRITTEN AND ILLUSTRATED
BY WALTER LINSENMAIER

THE ODYSSEY PRESS · NEW YORK

In this scene from a Brazilian rain forest, most of what appear to be leaves are actually insects—an example of the natural phenomenon known as camouflage.

INSECTS—those tiny, fragile, wriggling, fluttering, hopping creatures—are the secret rulers of the earth. If the insects were to die, all life on this planet would perish. First to go would be the flowering plants that insects pollinate; next, the plant-eating animals, and, finally, the flesh-eating animals. ■ Fortunately, there is little danger that the insects will die out. Eighty percent of the animals on earth are insects, and the number of insect species is greater than that of all other living animals. Some 750,000 insect species have already been classified, and more than 1 million may actually exist. The number of individual insects is almost impossible to estimate, but scientists have given us a few hints: they believe, for example, that the weight of all the insects in Africa would exceed that of all other African animals. ■ Insects have been on earth for a long time—perhaps as long as 350 million years—and to survive they have had to be hardy and extremely adaptable. Their capacity to reproduce is amazing; a queen bee, for example, may lay a million eggs during her lifetime. They have learned to live everywhere except in the oceans. They have become weavers, tailors, spinners, and builders. They can make silk, paper, wax, honey, and paste, and some species cultivate their own gardens. They can cope with almost any material. Certain wasps, for instance, chew holes in artillery shells so that they can enter and build their nests. ■ Insects have developed in an enormous variety of shapes and sizes. Among the largest is a moth with a wingspan of almost 1 foot,

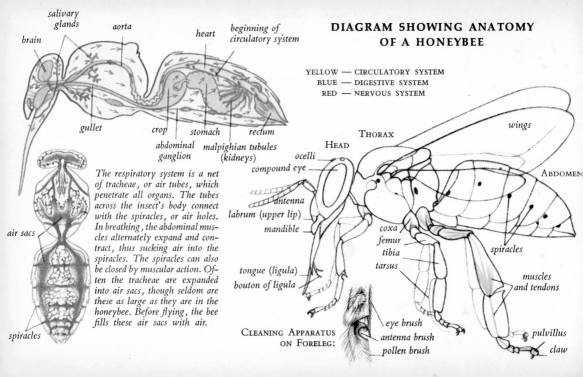

DIAGRAM SHOWING ANATOMY OF A HONEYBEE

YELLOW — CIRCULATORY SYSTEM
BLUE — DIGESTIVE SYSTEM
RED — NERVOUS SYSTEM

The respiratory system is a net of tracheae, or air tubes, which penetrate all organs. The tubes across the insect's body connect with the spiracles, or air holes. In breathing, the abdominal muscles alternately expand and contract, thus sucking air into the spiracles. The spiracles can also be closed by muscular action. Often the tracheae are expanded into air sacs, though seldom are these as large as they are in the honeybee. Before flying, the bee fills these air sacs with air.

CLEANING APPARATUS ON FORELEG:

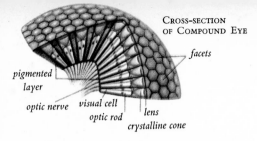

CROSS-SECTION OF COMPOUND EYE

facets

pigmented layer

optic nerve   visual cell   lens
        optic rod   crystalline cone

SOME SENSORY CELLS OF THE ANTENNAE.
The pore-plates (1), funnel shaped pores covered with a permeable membrane, and the sensory cones (2) are olfactory organs. The antenna bristles (3) are tactile organs.

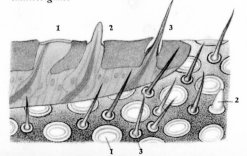

and a walkingstick that measures 9 inches in length. At the other end of the scale is a butterfly whose body is smaller than the insect collector's mounting pin (a cactus needle is used instead), and a minute parasitic wasp that can rest comfortably on the head of a pin. ■ In recent years, insects have given still another demonstration of their adaptability. Some of them have developed a resistance to the most powerful poisons men have devised to control them. With such adaptability, with their tremendous numbers and prolificity, it seems likely that insects will be on earth for a long time to come. ■ But what, exactly, is an insect? The name itself provides us with a clue; it comes from the Latin *insectum*, meaning "cut in." Entomology, the study of insects, comes from the Greek word *entomos*, which also means "cut in." And "cut in" is an accurate description, for in a mature insect the three parts of the body—head, thorax, and abdomen—are almost always separated by clearly defined incisions. ∎ Scientists have placed insects in the phylum *Arthropoda*, animals with jointed legs, along with spiders, ticks, millipedes, centipedes, and crustaceans. Within this phylum, they have been placed in the class Insecta, whose members include all six-legged animals. ∎ The ancestor of all insects was perhaps a many-segmented creature of the Paleozoic Era; it may have resembled a centipede or millipede. No fossil records of these first insects have been found, but there are fossil remains of insects from the Pennsylvanian Period of some 300 million years ago. Fossil remains include some highly evolved forms such as the *Meganeura*, which is related to the dragonfly and had a wingspan of about 28 to 40 inches. ∎ One reason insects have been so successful in the struggle

INCOMPLETE METAMORPHOSIS
(no pupal stage)

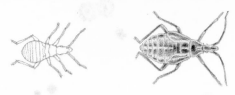

COMPLETE METAMORPHOSIS

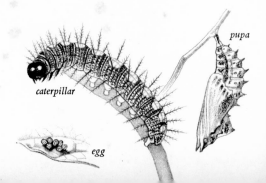

caterpillar

pupa

egg

The barbeiro of South America

The mourning cloak butterfly of North America

adult

for existence is their physical structure, which is far less fragile than it appears. Unlike vertebrates, insects wear their skeletons on the outside. Their muscles and organs are suspended within a hard exoskeleton. This outer shell is divided into small membrane-connected segments, so that the whole remains movable. Such a structure automatically limits the size to which insects can develop, but smallness may be an important factor in insect survival. ■ An insect's nervous system starts with a brain located in the head and proceeds as a series of ganglia, which look like a knotted string or a rope ladder, along the thorax and abdomen. ■ The circulatory system consists of an aorta—a simple tube, with a tubular heart at the posterior end. The heart takes in blood, usually greenish in color, through openings and pumps it forward through the aorta. The aorta ends in an open-

ing at the insect's head. There the blood streams out and flows backward through the body to bathe the organs. ■ The insect breathes through spiracles, or air-holes, which are found along the sides of its body. ■ The six slender, tubular legs of an insect contain internal muscles, and are usually divided into five main divisions: coxa, trochanter, femur, tibia, and tarsus. But within this basic form, insect legs vary greatly according to function. They may be adapted for jumping, swimming, climbing, grasping, digging, or spinning. Legs and feet may also include apparatus for cleaning, for collecting food, for piercing or snipping, and sometimes even for tasting or hearing. Insect feet almost always end in two claws, which often have a pulvillus, or pad, between them. In some species, this pad acts as a suction cup and enables the insect to hold fast or to move

LEFT: *The most colorful specimens of the beautifully sculptured harlequin beetle are found in Brazil.* ABOVE: *The metallic colors of the cuckoo wasps are structural—created by diffraction of light on the surface of the insect's body. Cuckoo wasps, or gold wasps, as they are sometimes called, are small insects, ranging from 1/10 of an inch to about 1½ inches in length.*

An iridescent cuckoo, or gold wasp, of California. Its colors are created when rays of light are broken up by the complicated microscopic structures in its chitinous surface. LEFT: detail of enlarged body, enlarged about 40 times. Cuckoo wasps are so named because they lay their eggs in the nests or on the larva of other insects.

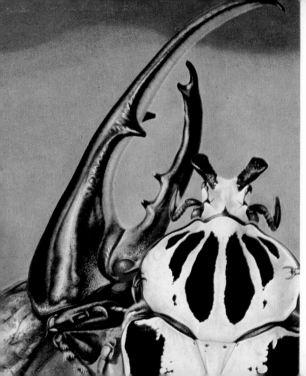

about on smooth surfaces. ■ The antennae are unusually delicate sensory instruments. The insect uses them to detect the faintest odors and the slightest vibrations. By smelling and probing with them, the insect is able to get an impression of the forms of its environment and to identify its own kind as well as other kinds of insects. ■ The insect's two compound eyes are made up of thousands of facets—tiny, individual, telescopic eyes—as many as 30,000 in each eye of some insects. With these eyes an insect can see in all directions. It can also see color, including ultraviolet, which is invisible to humans. Strangely enough, most insects, except for a few butterflies and flies, cannot see reds that lack an ultraviolet tone.

The longest and the largest beetles. The Hercules, with the large curved horns, sometimes reaches a length of 6 inches. It lives in Central and South America. The African goliath beetle, often 4 inches long, feeds on dung.

Many insects have simple eyes as well, but their function is not yet understood. ■ Unique to insects is the fascinating phenomenon of complete metamorphosis, the various transformations by which certain insects reach maturity. The caterpillar, for example, hatches from an egg as a larva, becomes a pupa, and eventually emerges as a butterfly. While incomplete metamorphosis exists elsewhere in the animal kingdom, the pupal, or cocoon, stage, which is the mark of complete metamorphosis, is found only in certain orders of insects. ■ The larval stage is usually the longest of an insect's life, lasting in some for several years. Many larvae do nothing but eat, pausing only to molt as their outer coverings become too

Fantastic insect forms of the Brazilian forest. Left to right: *a giant dynastid beetle; a true bug with leaf-like shapes on its hind legs; an owlet moth with a fringe of hair; and, below, a brightly colored scarab beetle.*

small. Molting is controlled by the release of certain hormones within the insect's body. Other larvae stop eating for a period of rest, called a diapause, which is usually related to climatic conditions. One example of a diapause is a winter hibernation. ■ The life-span of adult insects is often short, lasting from a few hours to a season, although there are some kinds that live for several years. During its adult stage, the primary purpose of the insect is to mate and to lay eggs. There are, of course, exceptions. Some insects do not lay eggs but give birth to tiny larvae. And among the termites, there are those that bring forth insects like themselves, metamorphosis having taken place within the mother's body.

LEFT: *South American tree hoppers. The grotesque outgrowth on the thorax serves no known biological purpose.* RIGHT: *In resting position, these Brazilian moths resemble spiders, beetles, and scorpions—a protection against would-be predators, known as mimicry.*

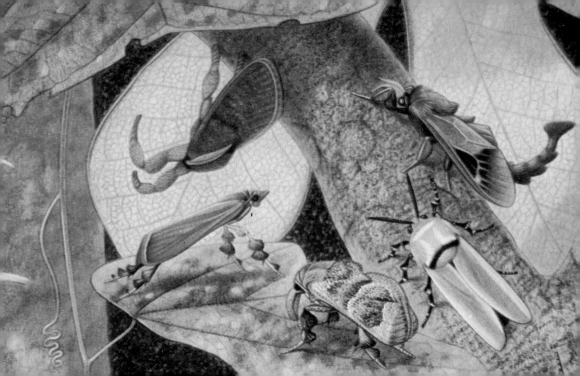

■ Incomplete metamorphosis occurs in many kinds of insects, including cockroaches, grasshoppers, and dragonflies. In this type of metamorphosis there is no pupal stage. The young look like miniature adults but have undeveloped wings and reproductive organs. These parts develop with successive molts. ■ Some insects that metamorphose in this manner have amazing powers of regeneration—they can replace lost legs at the time of molt. This ability, however, lasts only until maturity. ■ As a class, the insects are probably the most diversified in appearance of all creatures. Their world is fascinating to observe for the multiplicity of its forms, the richness of its colors, and the peculiarities of its designs. Many of their forms are extraordinary, and some even bizarre. ■ The basic material of the insect's exoskeleton is chitin, a hard substance of complex composition. The wing scales are also formed of chitin. In most adult insects, chitin is yellowish-,

Probably one of the most completely camouflaged of all insects is this bark louse. It is related to the book louse, which is among the smallest of all insects, measuring less than 1/25 of an inch. The book louse eats book bindings.

reddish-, or blackish-brown, but it can also be colorless or opaque. ■ Two kinds of colors are found in insects. The first comes from pigments which are usually variations of black, brown, red, and yellow. They are derived from the insect's blood or fat. The pigments may be impregnated in and on the chitinous exoskeleton, or closely under it. They may even be imbedded in the insect's internal organs and visible through transparent chitin. An inexhaustible wealth of color combinations is also produced by pigment granules laid in layers of unequal thickness. Most insect pigments cannot tolerate much light, and even in a living insect, they often fade in full sunlight. ■ The second and most

These tropical insects have the appearance of twigs, vines, leaves, and lichens. Insects so camouflaged tend to rest in places where their protective coloring will be most effective.

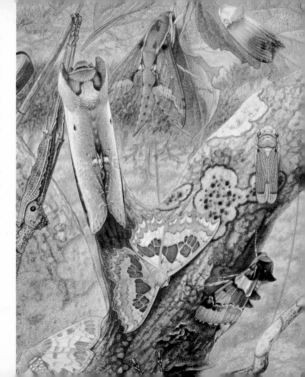

BELOW: *A tiny grasshopper which, when at rest, looks like a grain of earth. Many grasshoppers have colors that match the surroundings in which they are most commonly found.* RIGHT: *Brazilian moths which have light and dark patterns on their wings. These color contrasts successfully break up the insect's body contour when it is at rest. The moth below is a noctuid of Brazil. It belongs to the family Noctuidae, so named because of the "night owl" habits of most of its members. Many noctuid or owlet moths have light and dark, or cryptic, color patterns on their wings.*

Brazilian moth at left flashes brightly colored hindwings to scare an enemy. Moth at right resembles a poisonous caterpillar.

magnificent kind of insect colors—the glittering silvers, golds, greens, blues, and whites—are structural colors, caused by the diffraction of light as it is broken up by the complicated microscopic structures in the insect's chitinous surface. All structural colors change according to the angle at which the light falls on the insect. ■ There are also insects, such as the fireflies, whose luminosity derives from chemically altered albuminous cells in their bodies. ■ In general, colors are thought to protect the insects from too much light and heat, while hair and scales are useful in slowing down the loss of warmth and moisture from

23

the body. ■ The strange forms of the insect world—the horns, the crenellations, the projections—are innumerable. In some instances they seem to serve no useful purpose, but generally they help to protect the species. ■ Many insects instinctively employ their shapes and colors to camouflage themselves when they are at rest and most vulnerable. They take their rest in surroundings which best aid their camouflage, and assume the most effective positions. The contrast of light and dark shades may break up identifiable body contours and make the insects almost invisible; or they may resemble leaves, branches, stems, thorns, pebbles, rotten wood, or even seeds and nuts that have

The warning colors of the caterpillar and the white butterfly at left, and the red fire bugs at right, show predators that these insects are either poisonous or bad-tasting. The tree hoppers, at left, are perfectly edible; their gaudy colors are only a "bluff."

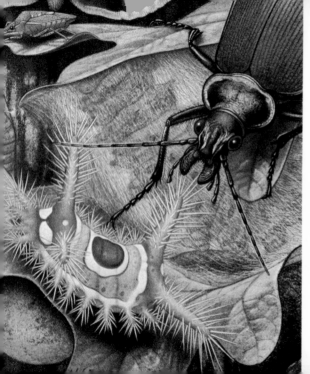

fallen to the ground. ■ Some insects, inconspicuous while resting, may suddenly flash brightly colored wings, abdomens, or eyespots when threatened by an enemy. These unexpected "flashing colors" may distract the would-be attacker just long enough for the insect to make its escape. ■ Other insects with warning colors never try to hide their presence or to flee from danger; their colors warn enemies that their body juices are poisonous or bad-tasting, or that their bodies are covered with poisonous hairs. ■ Some edible insects are protected from enemies by their resemblance to inedible species. Scientists refer to such protection as mimicry. Mimicry may include

The bristling spines of the saddleback moth caterpillar of North America, which protect it from most predators, fail to keep off an attack by a beetle of the genus Calosoma.

Mimicry in the insect world: Assassin bug, at upper right, is like aggressive wasp, at left, in appearance and movement. Butterfly and beetle, both harmless, closely resemble poisonous beetle resting between them. Resting on the oval leaf, at center, is an insect that lives with ants and resembles them closely.

form and behavior as well as markings. A number of harmless beetles, butterflies, flies, bugs, and grasshoppers, for example, look much like aggressive wasps; they frighten off their foes by behaving as if they were wasps ready to sting at the slightest provocation. ■ In addition to the various forms of protective coloring, insects have instinctive habits which further insure their safety and survival. Among insects are found masons, potters, diggers, miners, and model-makers, all of which carry on their trade without ever having served an apprenticeship. Their principal tools are their astonishingly differentiated mouth-parts, a marvelous collection of instruments that might well arouse the envy of human surgeons, craftsmen, or burglars. The mouth-parts vary from a harmless tongue used for sucking nectar to others adapted to boring, sawing, clamping, or cutting. Some even take the forms of poi-

BITING—SUCKING

grasshopper   *beetle*

house fly

LICKING—SUCKING

bee

sonous hypodermics and murderous pincers. These mouth-parts are, in many cases, supplemented by appropriate structures on the forelegs. ■ Insects eat almost everything. Many feed only on certain plants, even on only one particular part of a plant; others are less fussy in their diet. Some species are herbivorous, others carnivorous, and still others omnivorous. Some insects are carnivorous in the larval stage but, when mature, feed only on nectar. ■ Close biological interrelationships between organisms play an important part in the insect world as, indeed, they do throughout nature. For instance, aphids, or plant lice, which suck juice from plants, are in turn sucked of their juices by the larvae of the hover fly. Adult hover flies, which sip nectar from flowers, are caught by certain digger wasps, stung into paralysis, and carried to the wasp's burrow as food for the young. But there

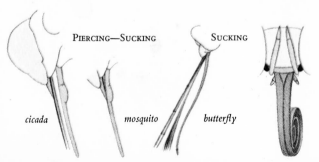

PIERCING—SUCKING

SUCKING

cicada

mosquito

butterfly

INSECT MOUTH PARTS

Color Code

○ —*face plate (clypeus)*

◗ —*upper lip (labrum)*

◗ —*lower lip (labium) with segmented feelers\ (labial palpi)*

● —*upper jaw (mandible)*

◗ —*lower jaw (maxilla) with segmented feelers (maxillary palpi)*

◗ —*tongue (ligula)*

29

are also mighty robber flies which sting digger wasps and suck out *their* body juices. Still other insects, such as ants, protect whole herds of aphids and even take them into their nests in order to eat the sweetish juice, called honeydew, which the aphids secrete. ■ Although the presence of most insects is not unfavorable to that of man, certain insects do carry diseases. The organism that causes the disease is taken into the insect's proboscis while it is sucking blood from an infected animal or person, and then injected into the next victim the insect bites. Typical disease-carrying insects of this kind are the African tsetse fly and the anopheles mosquito, the first a vector in

Eaters sometimes become the eaten in the insect world. Aphids, which live on plants, are sucked dry of their body juices by other insects, including the larvae of the hover fly. The adult hover fly (right) may become food for the larvae of digger wasps, which are eaten by robber flies.

Both the male and the female of the African tsetse fly, a vector in the transmission of sleeping sickness, suck blood from humans and cattle. These insects may take as much as six times their own body weight in their victim's blood. Tsetse flies are found only in Africa.

sleeping sickness, the second in malaria. ■ The most important role played by insects in the natural community is that of pollinator of flowers. There are wonderful adaptations of both plants and insects for the accomplishment of this purpose; sometimes the adaptations are carried to a point where only one group of insects can pollinate a particular kind of flower. For instance, the nectar of the trumpet-shaped honeysuckle flower lies so deep that only insects with very long tongues, like the hawk moths, the bumblebees, and the anthophorid bees, can reach it. ■ A curious but highly functional relationship exists between certain orchids and certain bees and wasps. Because of a combination of color, shape, and possibly scent, these flowers look like female wasps and bees, thus attracting the male insects and ensuring pollination. For this reason such orchids —actually orchises—are called "fetish flowers."

The anopheles mosquito, which carries malaria, differs from the culex mosquito in having longer maxillary palpi associated with the proboscis. At rest it takes a more humped position. The anopheles larva floats horizontally in the water while the culex larva hangs head down from the surface. Only the female is the carrier, because it feeds on blood, which it needs for the eggs to mature. The organism which causes malaria enters the victim's blood stream and multiplies in the red blood corpuscles, eventually causing their breakdown. When these corpuscles break down, the victim gets the chills and high fever characteristic of the disease.

■ Another type of relationship exists between the plant and insects that make galls. The gall-makers—gall wasps, sawflies, and certain beetles—by laying eggs on a plant are able to induce it to produce an abnormal growth known as a gall, which then provides food and shelter for the insect's larvae. ■ The most amazing examples of instinctual behavior in the insect world are seen in the precautions these creatures take to ensure the welfare of their offspring. After

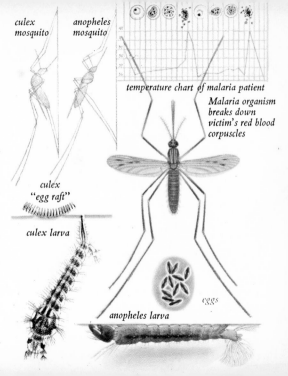

culex
mosquito

anopheles
mosquito

temperature chart of malaria patient

Malaria organism breaks down victim's red blood corpuscles

culex "egg raft"

culex larva

eggs

anopheles larva

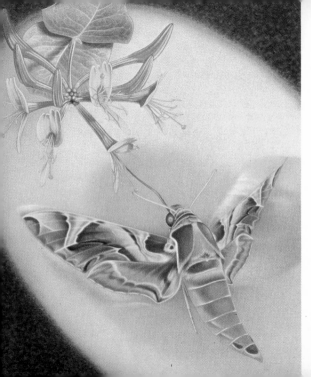

mating occurs, the female unerringly finds the right place to lay her eggs, often laying them on just the right food plant for the young. If the insect is parasitic, the female, with deadly purpose, will seek out the host and deposit her eggs within the host's body. ■ Most insects leave their eggs after laying them, but earwigs and some beetles stay nearby to watch over them. Ants and termites also guard the eggs laid in their colonies, keeping them in special brood chambers. These eggs are moved from chamber to chamber when there are changes in temperature and humidity. Some digger wasps sting and paralyze caterpillars, grasshoppers, crickets, or cicadas, and then store them in holes in the ground or in wood. The wasps lay

Only an insect with a very long tongue, such as this hawk moth, can reach the nectar of the deep flowers of the honeysuckle. A powerful scent is emitted from these flowers just at dusk when the hawk moths are most actively hunting food.

The female of the summer generation of the oak gall wasp deposits her eggs in the veins of the oak leaf. A gall grows at the site where she has punctured the leaf. The larva lives in the center of the gall and feeds on it until it reaches maturity. From such larvae come a generation of wasps consisting solely of females. These mature during the winter and lay their eggs in dormant oak buds. Then galls are formed which look like oak buds. Inside these galls a bisexual summer generation of oak gall wasps develops.

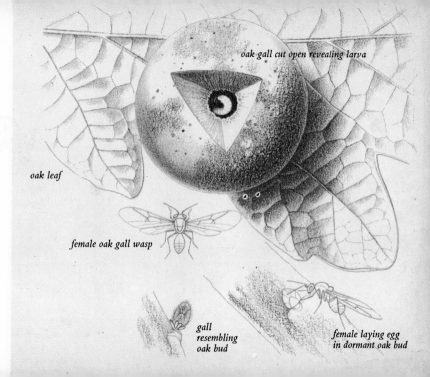

oak gall cut open revealing larva

oak leaf

female oak gall wasp

gall resembling oak bud

female laying egg in dormant oak bud

their eggs on their paralyzed victims, thus providing a food supply for their offspring in the larval stage. ■ Other bees and wasps, even solitary ones, build ingenious cellular structures, with one cell for each egg. Sometimes these brood chambers are made separately, but many species make them as combs. Some bees and wasps build their combs out of pebbles, or out of soil and sand. Leaf-cutter bees cut round pieces out of leaves and flowers, which they carry to the nest. After carpeting the entrance with this plant material, they next build a series of cells, one on top of the other. ■ The wool bee uses plant-down stripped from leaves and stems to

LEFT: *Two digger wasps of the California desert. The one at the right is dragging a cricket which it has stung into paralysis to its burrow. Above it, a wool bee is just hatching.* RIGHT: *A digger wasp about to sting a grub. The wasp will then deposit its egg on the grub.*

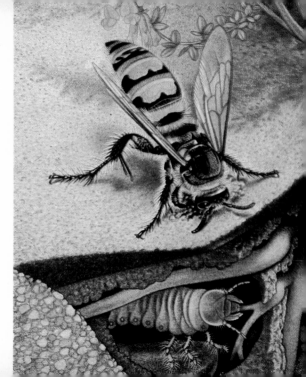

build its nest. When it has finished a cell and laid a banana-shaped egg in it, the bee collects pollen and nectar in its abdominal pouch and places this mixture on top of the egg. After the bee larva emerges, it feeds on the ball of pollen. But sometimes a parasitic cuckoo wasp will lay its egg in the bee cell while the female bee is out looking for pollen. Then the cuckoo wasp larva, which hatches after the bee larva has matured, will gradually suck the bee larva dry, killing it. From the downy nest will emerge not a wool bee, but a cuckoo wasp. ■ The beginnings of social behavior are found among a variety of insects. The female of the burying

The wool bee builds its nest out of plant down. The bee lays her banana-shaped eggs in separate cells. Then she collects a combination of pollen and nectar, which she shapes into a ball and places in the cell. When the larva hatches from the egg, it feeds on the pollen ball.

beetle feeds its young in the nest. One of the horned beetles has a kind of family life—parents and larvae live together and seem to communicate by chirping sounds. ■ But the honeybees, ants, and termites are the true social insects. Within their societies, which can go on for decades, the insects live in a caste system usually based on the division between the sexually endowed members and the asexual members. The former are queens and males, or drones; the latter are workers and, in ant and termite societies, soldiers. The manifold tasks of such societies are performed by castes, each adapted to carry out only certain specific

Two bumblebees and, left, a solitary bee which resembles a bumblebee. Bumblebees build their colonies underground. These colonies last for only a season; the males and workers die when cold weather comes. Only the queen overwinters. Bumblebees have longer tongues than most other bees.

tasks. ■ These insects work together for the preservation of their state, creating young queens as needed and protecting their own against enemy attack. Ants and termites go on slave raids to rob other societies of "slave" insects in order to increase their own work force. They also appear to enjoy the pleasures of alcohol, which they obtain from the body juices of certain beetles. ■ The engineering accomplishments of social insects are incredible—they have mastered problems of stress and strain, of ventilation, of heating, and, in some cases, of water supply. They take care of the brood, keep their nests clean, and store food.

An ant colony is established by a fertilized queen. She then tears off her wings and begins laying eggs. She is larger than the other members of the colony. The workers are sterile females. They take care of the eggs, gather food, feed members of the colony, and build the quarters.

Leaf-cutter ants even raise their own vegetables. ■ Scientists now know that these insects communicate by sounds and signs, by their antennae, and by mass dances. But there is still much to be learned about these insect societies and the individual and collective behavior within them. ■ So great is the insect's adaptability that its kind can survive and increase almost anywhere on earth. They are found on snow and ice, in burning deserts, on windy mountains, in the dark stillness of caves, in plants, and within the bodies of other animals. ■ Many insects use fresh water either as a medium in which to develop or as an adult environment. They live in clear, cold mountain lakes as well as in warm, swampy ponds. Indeed, some are found in warm springs where the temperature is 131° F. ■ Adaptation to a watery environment is one of the most remarkable achievements in the insect world. Oxygen

is taken from the water through the integument or through the gills of the insect's body. It may also be taken on the surface through the insect's spiracles, or even obtained from plants growing in the water. There are also many adaptations that prevent the insect from becoming wet, from sinking into the water, or from being swept away by the current of swiftly flowing streams. ■ One of the most difficult environments for the survival of life is found in caves, where light and oxygen are scarce. The retrogressed cave beetle no longer has eyes; its abdomen has become enlarged to form a balloon-like reservoir of air; and its legs and antennae have become abnormally long. ■ Few insects, of course, are found everywhere. Each kind needs its own specialized living space, and would perish in any other.

As larvae, dragonflies live in water and breathe through gills. As adults, they live on land. They are among the swiftest fliers of all insects.

The adaptability of insects is a trait of the orders, families, and genera. In contrast, the individual species are limited by very narrow and rigid conditions for existence. Thus, a slight change in climate or the disappearance of just one plant species may cause the extinction of a whole group of insects. ■ With the advance of civilization, and the destruction of so many kinds of environments, there are many species of insects that will disappear forever from the face of the earth. But when we hear the shrill insect voices that announce the arrival of spring, we remember that millions of years ago these were among the first live sounds to break the primordial stillness; perhaps millennia after man and the other animal orders have become extinct, these same voices will interrupt the silence of a deserted world.

A cave-dwelling beetle has an enlarged balloon-like abdomen in which it stores air. It has lost its eyes through generations of living in darkness.

INDEX

ABOUT THE BACK ENDSHEETS

The class Insecta is made up of some 30 orders. Each order is divided into families, each family into genera. Each genus contains at least one species, and often many species. Within the species there can be additional categories of subspecies and races. If one species is very widely distributed, or, conversely, is a poor flier, it is then very often subdivided into geographical races or subspecies. These are most, clearly distinguishable in island habitats where the insect has been isolated for long periods. Illustrated overleaf are 25 representatives of the most important orders of insects of the world.

1. Thysanura (bristletails) and 2. Collembola (springtails) are designated as primitive insects.
3. Ephemeroptera (mayflies) with larva.
4. Odonata (dragonflies) with larvae.
5. Blattaria (cockroaches) with young offspring.
6. Mantodea (mantids).
7. Isoptera (termites), female, male, worker, and soldier.
8. Plecoptera (stoneflies); larva at left.
9. Phasmidae (leaf insects and walkingsticks).
10. Orthoptera (grasshoppers and crickets).
11. Dermaptera (earwigs).
12. Corrodentia (booklice, barklice).
13. Anoplura (lice).
14. Thysanoptera (thrips).
15. Homoptera (cicadas, aphids).
16. Heteroptera (true bugs); at right a waterbug swimming on its back.
17. Neuroptera (lacewings), and, right, ant lion larva.
18. Mecoptera (scorpionflies), with larva.
19. Trichoptera (caddisflies) with larva in house.
20. Lepidoptera (moths, butterflies), with caterpillar and pupa.
21. Diptera (flies, mosquitoes) with larvae and pupal case.
22. Siphonaptera (fleas)
23. Coleoptera (beetles) with larvae.
24. Strepsiptera (twisted wings, stylops).
25. Hymenoptera (bees, wasps, ants) with larva.

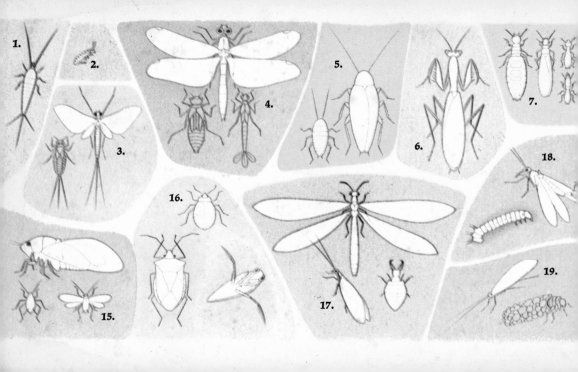